# Bow Wow! Meow!

## A First Book of Sounds

By MELANIE BELLAH
Pictures by TRINA SCHART

GOLDEN PRESS   NEW YORK

How does the kitty go?
Meow.

How does the doggie go?
Bow wow.

How does the cow go?
Moooo.

How does the rooster go?
Cock-a-doodle-doo.

How does the car go?
Beep-beep.

How does the chick go?
Peep-peep.

How does the siren go?
Oo-ooh, oo-ooh.

How does the train go?
Choo-choo-choo.

How does the duck go?
Quack, quack.

How does the trolley go?
Click-clack, click-clack.

How does the pigeon go?
Coo, coo.

How does the owl go?
Whoo.

How does the lamb go?
Baa, baa.

# Who's that laughing?
## Ha-ha-ha.

How does the bell go?
Ding-dong-ding.

How does the phone go?
Ting-aling-aling.

How does the horse go?
Neigh-hh.

How do the people go?
Hurray!

How does the bee go?
Bzzz.

How does the snake go?
Ssss.

How does the rain go?
Pitter-patter.

How does the monkey go?
Chatter-chatter.

How does the clock go?
Tick-tock, tick-tock.

Someone's at the door—
Knock, knock.

A baby is crying,
Boo-hoo-hoo.

A baby is playing,
Peek-a-boo.

How does the music go?
La-la-la.

How does the doll go?
Mama.

How does the wind go?
Whhh.

Let's be quiet:
Shhh.